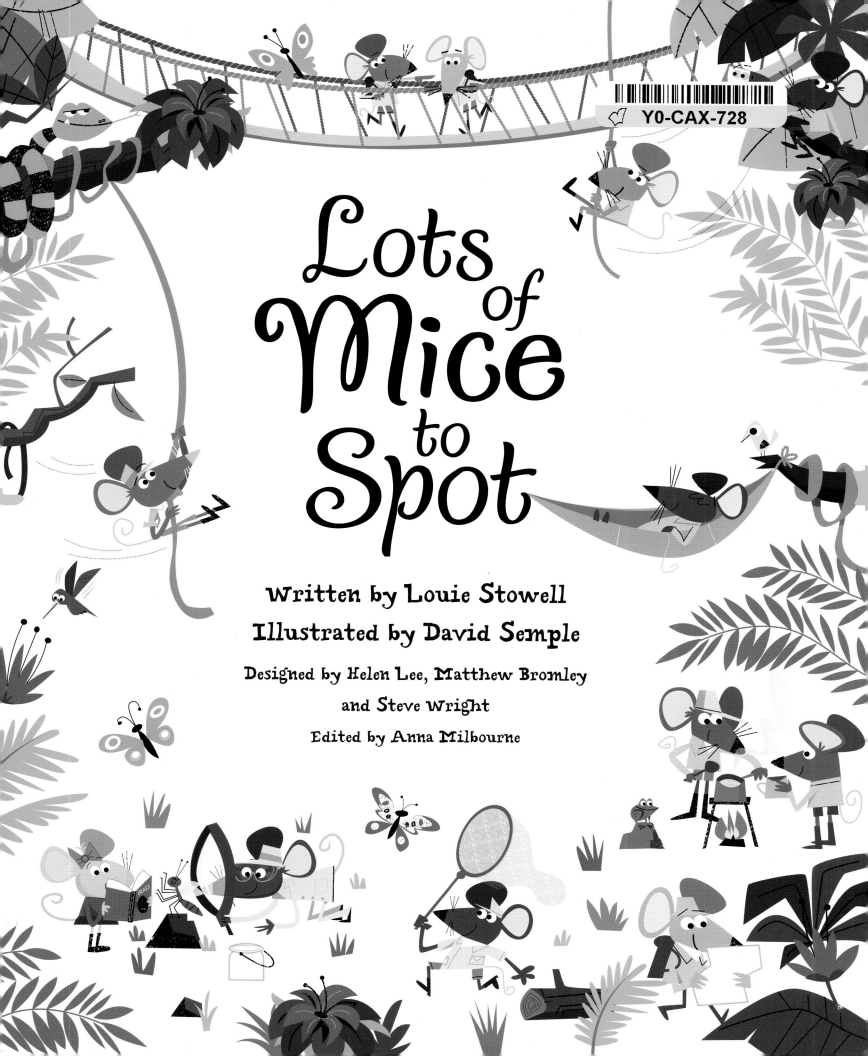

Lots of Mice to Spot

Written by Louie Stowell

Illustrated by David Semple

Designed by Helen Lee, Matthew Bromley
and Steve Wright

Edited by Anna Milbourne

Look at all the places you can find in this book. I want to go to the cheese factory. Yum!

Zoom to the cheese moon on pages 4-5.

Watch movies being made on pages 6-7.

Spot lots of crazy cars at the mouse races on pages 8-9.

Dive beneath the sea on pages 10-11.

Don't get lost in the jungle on pages 12-13.

Peep into mouse houses on pages 14-15.

The fair is in town on pages 16-17.

There's snow, mice and plenty of ice on pages 18-19.

Tour a cheese factory on pages 20-21.

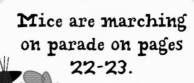

Mice are marching on parade on pages 22-23.

You'll find lots of games and puzzles on pages 24-30, and answers on pages 31-32.

Here are some friendly mice you'll see on every spread.

Lady Whiskerton is a wealthy mouse who likes the finer things in life.

Reggie Paintpaw loves drawing, painting and making sculptures.

Onika Edam is a scientist. She makes gadgets that go vroom, zoom and... KABOOM!

Old Algernon Cheddarton takes life at his own slow, sleepy pace.

Lily Pipsqueak is always reading, even if she's also busy doing something else.

Sheriff Sharpeye helps mice in need and fights crime. Sneaky cats beware!

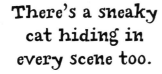

There's a sneaky cat hiding in every scene too.

Meow!

Mouse in a bathtub

Mouse lifting weights

Birthday cake

PUZZLES AND GAMES

You'll find stickers to use in these puzzles and games at the back of the book.

Use the stickers to match the fish to their shadows.

Here's something our teacher asked us to do at school today. Can you do it, too?

Put these cheeses in size order. Label the biggest one 1 and the smallest one 5.

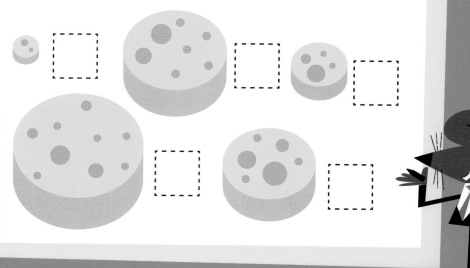

Join the dots to finish this picture.

Use the stickers to fill in this rocket. Watch out — they're all jumbled up.

Use the stickers to pack a lunch for me that's the same as my friend's.

Can you find the students of **Nibbleton School** and our teacher? We're in every scene on pages 4-23 and we all wear this badge.

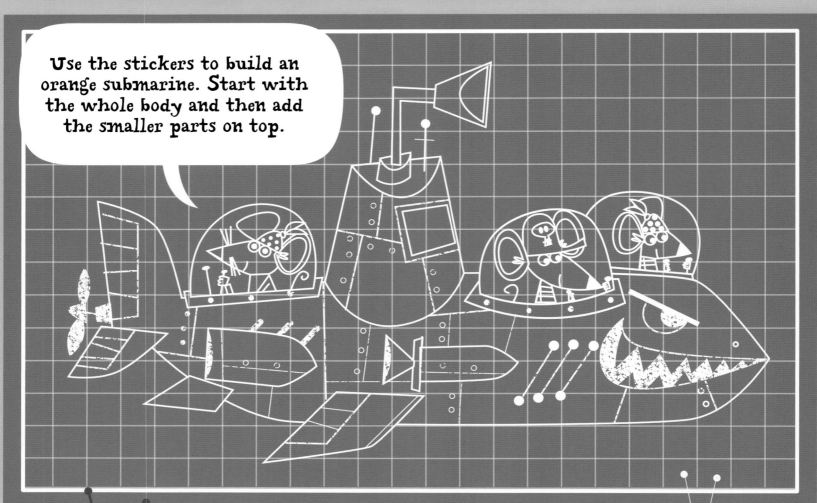

Use the stickers to build an orange submarine. Start with the whole body and then add the smaller parts on top.

Can you spot 10 differences between these two pictures?

Follow these trails to discover which house belongs to which racing mouse.

Then use the stickers to match the houses to each mouse's car.

Use the stickers to help me count out enough cheeses for each of my customers.

Algernon wants 3

Onika wants 4

Lily wants 2

Help Reggie finish his picture by filling it in with pencils or felt-tip pens.

Answers

4-5 Cheese moon

- Three planets have rings around them.
- Lady Whiskerton is pouring some tea.

- Blue spaceship
- Alien
- Lily's group of stars
- Matching flying saucer
- Shooting star
- Space radio
- Floating cheeseburger
- Space tennis ball
- Cheese flag

6-7 Mouse movies

- Two mice are hiding in barrels.
- Reggie is painting the scenery.
- Sheriff Sharpeye is catching bank robbers.

- Supermouse
- Mouse in a wolf suit
- Cameramouse in yellow
- Wind machine
- Tail end of the horse
- Knight costume
- Princess

8-9 Mouse races

- There are five mouse balloons.

- Cheesy snacks
- Team of mechanics
- Traffic lights
- Purple spare wheel
- Young mouse with toy car
- Cheeseburger car
- Shoe car
- Car in pond
- Wind-up mouse car

10-11 Beneath the sea

- Three anchors
- Eight puffer fish
- Four striped sea snakes
- Seven blue jellyfish
- Reggie is carving an underwater statue.

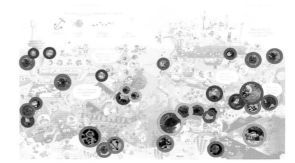

- Diver in an orange suit
- Six turtles
- Sunken treasure
- Matching fish

12-13 In the jungle

- Sheriff Sharpeye is rescuing the young mouse.
- There are nine purple flowers.

- Two mice with fishing rods
- Four mice with butterfly nets
- Three blue statues
- Eight hummingbirds
- Mice swimming
- Matching butterfly
- Three tents

14-15 Mouse houses

- There are four ladders.
- Algernon is dancing to music.

- Window cleaner
- Painting of Lady Whiskerton
- Mouse in a bathtub
- Mouse lifting weights
- Birthday cake
- Three pink rooms
- Lost ball
- Laundry

16-17 At the fair

- Algernon is looking at himself in a mirror.
- Reggie has painted five tiger faces.

- Juggler
- Green bumper car
- Baby mouse
- Lollipop mouse
- This is the mouse's balloon.
- Young mouse's daddy
- Mice with teddy bears

18-19 Snow mice

- The left-hand pile has more snowballs.
- Sheriff Sharpeye is flying a helicopter.

Differences

- Pink snowmobile
- Fallen skater
- Ski instructor
- Ice palace
- Skiers with red skis
- Lost hat
- Hot-chocolate stand

20-21 Cheese factory

- Lily made the milky footprints.
- Three mice are grating cheese.
- Two more triangles are needed to fill the shape.

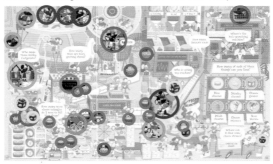

- Nine blue cheeses
- Six stinky cheeses
- Five cheese guides
- Seven milk churns
- Cracker nibbler
- Three cheese stirrers
- One boss mouse
- Hole-punching machine
- Cheese straws

22-23 Mice on parade

- Lady Whiskerton is the Cheese Queen.
- There are five red bikes.

- Bucket of moon cheese
- Big-horn player
- Mermouse
- Cheesy milkshakes
- Lost flag
- Matching helmet
- Eight drummers

Games

Fish matched to their shadows

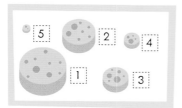

Cheeses in size order

Here's what the spaceship should look like.

This is what the completed submarine should look like.

Ten differences

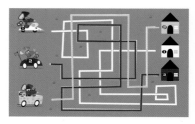

This shows who lives where.

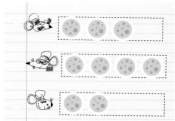

Cheeses for each customer

Use these stickers on pages 24-25.

Put each of these fish on top of the shadow that they match.

 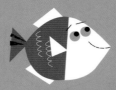   

Stick all these stickers on the drawing of the rocket in the top right-hand corner of page 25. Look carefully at the stickers to see which one fits where.

Use these stickers to pack a lunch that matches the full lunchbox. You can use the spare stickers anywhere you like.

 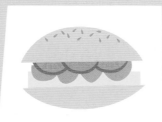    

Use these stickers on pages 26-27.

Use these small ones anywhere you like

Do you like my crown?

I'm a monster!

Yee-hah!

Lady Whiskerton's costume

Lily's costume

Sheriff Sharpeye's costume

Some of the party guests have put on the bottom halves of their costumes. Add these headdresses and helmets to complete their outfits.

Add these to the red food table.

Decorate the tables with this bunting.

Put these on the yellow drinks table.

Use these stickers on pages 26-27.

Use these small ones anywhere you like

Cheese moon here I come!

Wooooo!

Reggie to the rescue!

Algernon's costume

Onika's spooky costume

Reggie's super costume

Use these stickers to add guests and decorate the party scene.

Use these stickers on pages 28-29.

Step 1
Main body

Step 2
Propeller

Step 3
Periscope

Step 4
Face

Step 5
Boosters

Step 6
Pirate crew

Match each house to the mouse racer who lives there.

Please put the correct number of cheeses next to my customers. Thank you!